BIG
MISS
LIBERTY

By the same author

5000 Years of Stargazing
Painted Rock to Printed Page
Lens Magic

In collaboration with Alice Beard

The Birthday of a Nation: July 4, 1776
Old Liberty Bell
Heels, Wheels and Wire
5000 Years of Glass
5000 Years of Gems and Jewelry

BIG MISS LIBERTY

BY

FRANCES ROGERS

Illustrated by
the author

J. B. LIPPINCOTT COMPANY

PHILADELPHIA NEW YORK

Fifteenth Printing

Library of Congress catalog card number: 38-27666

Printed in the United States of America

ILLUSTRATIONS

INTRODUCING MISS LIBERTY TO YOU

If you are not already acquainted with the big statue that stands in New York Harbor (you may have seen her, but have you more than a bowing acquaintance with her?) this story—a true one, mind—is by way of introduction, so that when you do, some day, call on Miss Liberty, you will be able to regard her as an old friend.

BIG
MISS
LIBERTY

Inscription engraved on a tablet within the main entrance of the pedestal:

THE NEW COLOSSUS

Not like the brazen giant of Greek fame,
With conquering limbs astride from land to land.
Here at our sea-washed, sunset gates shall stand
A mighty woman with a torch, whose flame
Is the imprisoned lightning, and her name
Mother of exiles. From her beacon-hand
Glows world wide welcome; her mild eyes command
The air-bridged harbor that twin cities frame.
"Keep ancient lands, your storied pomp!" cries she
With silent lips. "Give me your tired, your poor,
Your huddled masses yearning to breathe free.
The wretched refuse of your teeming shore.
Send these, the homeless, tempest-tost to me.
I lift my lamp beside the golden door!"

—Emma Lazarus, 1849-1887

ONCE UPON A time there was a man who had an idea that kept buzzing about in his head. And since it would not keep still long enough for him to get a good look at it—to find out what sort of an idea it was—he just went ahead with his work.

Now his work was the making of statuary, for this man—Auguste—was an artist. He had cut, from stone, many statues of generals and other war heroes.

One day that little idea that kept buzzing about in his head, did settle down for a brief rest, but it landed in the *back* of his mind—just out of reach. Auguste could feel it but he still couldn't make out what it was.

"Dear me," he sighed. "I'm tired of making portraits of men—just men, even if they are war heroes, and famous."

"You want, maybe, to make a statue of a lady?" asked Pierre.

Pierre was the boy apprentice who mixed clay for Auguste.

"Well, yes and no," answered Auguste. "Yes—a woman, perhaps; but no—not just any woman."

The artist rubbed his brow. The idea stirred and moved forward a little.

Auguste blinked at Pierre. "I wonder . . ." he began. "You know, I almost think it is that I would like to model a figure that would be so big that . . . that . . ."

He hesitated.

"That it would stick way up higher than all the trees!" exclaimed Pierre.

"Why—yes!" agreed Auguste.

Then in a dreamy voice he continued: "A towering figure . . . clouds would encircle its brow like a wreath of . . . of . . ."

"Would you make it as big as the celebrated Colossus of Rhodes?" asked Pierre.

"Pooh! The Colossus of Rhodes indeed! That would be no more than knee-high to the figure I'd like to . . . um . . ."

But now the little idea left its perch and began buzzing about again in Auguste's head.

"What figure, Monsieur?"

"Oh, I don't know. . . ." Auguste frowned. "What I was going to say has slipped my mind." Then, "Come! come! boy," he exclaimed briskly. "Get some wet cloths over the clay—it must not dry out. Have you nothing to do but talk, talk!"

Auguste snatched off his black velvet béret and flung it into a corner, and he hauled his linen smock up over his head and tossed it after his béret.

"Fetch me my cape and hat, boy. I'm in no mood for further work, it seems. But tonight . . . ah, tonight I shall visit with my good friend, Edouard de Laboulaye. Perhaps that will give me inspiration. A number of us dine tonight at Versailles."

With a smile at his little apprentice, Auguste swung the long black cape about his shoulders, picked up gloves and cane and cocked his tall silk hat on the side of his head.

Suddenly the idea buzzed for an instant right across the front of his mind.

"It would be the biggest statue in the world," he said wistfully as he looked at the boy.

Now Pierre, of course, knew nothing about the little idea that kept teasing his master and so he was not in the least prepared for what happened the very next morning.

He had arrived at the big studio at the usual early hour, and had expected to get his various tasks done in the usual way before the master appeared—which might be any time between half past ten and noon.

But at nine o'clock sharp—Pierre knew the time because the bell in the church had just tolled the hour—at nine o'clock, Pierre had been in the courtyard. He had just emptied a can of water on the tall plant in the green box, when he heard the gate squeak protestingly.

Auguste had come! and was already rushing across the court and into the studio.

"Boy!" he shouted excitedly. "Collect my water-colors and brushes! Get my sketch-pads together. I must see what supplies need replacing. Probably one cannot easily get colors over there!"

"WHAT FIGURE MONSIEUR?"

Pierre put down the heavy brass watering-can and followed Auguste into the studio. The boy did not hurry. It seemed silly, he thought, to get so excited about a little sketching trip into the country.

"Will you be gone all day, Monsieur?" he asked.

"All day, indeed!" shouted Auguste. "One does not go to America and return by sunset!" What could the little goose be thinking of?

"Listen, Pierre. I may be gone for months!"

Pierre's jaw dropped in amazement.

"Yes, boy. As soon as I can manage it, I'm off to the New World on a mission that suits me down to the ground. I shall travel from the Atlantic coast to the Golden West. . . ." Auguste spread wide both arms. "I shall visit the people of the southland in the vast new republic . . . and talk with the people of the north. . . ."

He dropped his arms and looked at Pierre. "Do you understand, boy?"

"No, Monsieur, not at all."

Auguste laughed. "No wonder," he said.

"I'll admit I scarcely take it all in myself. But I'll try to make it clearer. It's like this, Pierre. For more than five years a group of us have been discussing what we, as a nation, could give to the United States of America to express our good will and fellowship toward our sister republic. It should be something symbolic of democracy. In short, a statue. And I have been commissioned to go to America to look over the ground so that I may judge what kind of a statue will be most fitting. . . . Now do you understand?"

"Well, not much, Monsieur—except that you are going to America."

Auguste groaned and rubbed his brow.

The little idea in the back of his mind had been very quiet for some time, but now it began buzzing gently.

A dreamy expression crept into the artist's eyes.

"Some kind of a symbol . . . a symbol of light. . . ."

Then he looked down at the boy.

"Suppose," he went on, "it were a statue —a great towering statue looming high above green trees . . . in a park—a park in Boston or in New York. . . .

"Oh, well—we'll see," said Auguste, becoming practical once more.

And so it came about that one sunny day in 1871, Pierre was standing with a crowd of people on the long platform in the Paris railway station.

He heard the high toot of the train whistle . . . he heard the cheering of the people . . . and through misty eyes he saw the train slide away down the track.

The train was bound for the coast where one boarded the boat for America, and it carried Pierre's beloved master, Auguste Bartholdi.

All the way across the Atlantic the weather was fine, and Auguste thoroughly enjoyed pacing the deck of the good ship, *Pireire*. He liked the salt spray that wet his cheeks when he stood in the bow and watched the blue water. But best of all, he liked the hours spent in his little cabin below decks, when he was making sketch after sketch and thinking about what sort of statue would be suitable as a gift from his people, the French, to the American people.

Every day the little idea that had been buzzing about in the back of his mind, would edge just a bit nearer to the front.

"I've *almost* got it," he would murmur each time he began a new sketch, "almost—but not quite."

Then one day when Auguste came up on deck, he found the sky full of wheeling gulls. They circled around the ship and screamed as they swooped to the water to catch up scraps of food flung out by the cook's boy.

And while Auguste stood there watching the gulls and thinking how fine they were when the sun gleamed on their strong white wings, someone shouted, *"Land!"*

Yes, there it was—a hazy blue streak on the horizon. That was land—the land of America.

No more sketching for Auguste. He, like the other voyagers, turned all his attention on the narrow blue strip that gradually widened and grew ever more clear while he watched.

And when the big ship steamed into the bay, and New York Harbor loomed before his eyes, Auguste became quite breathless with excitement. The little idea was fairly whirling about in his head, more violently than ever before. . . .

Then suddenly—without further warning —it swooped down and came to rest right in the front of Auguste's mind.

For the first time he could see it clearly!

Instead of being little, it was tremendous.

With his mind's eye he saw the towering figure of a gigantic and stately woman. In one hand she held a great torch—held it high against the sky. Gulls circled and flashed white around her crowned head. There she stood—a symbol of light—welcoming newcomers to the Land of Liberty.

"Liberty," murmured Auguste. "Liberty enlightening the world."

He rubbed his brow, but the idea did not budge. It had taken firm hold right in the front of his mind, where he could see it clearly.

With both hands, Auguste clutched the railing and braced himself.

Things were happening almost too fast for him to endure.

Not only had he now thought of exactly the right gift for the French people to give to the Americans, but now—at this very moment—he was looking at the very spot where he would like to have the giant statue stand.

The ship was passing a small island. A compact bit of green land it was, and its name, a fellow traveler told him, was "Bedloe's Island."

"Great place for rabbits," said the traveler. "Yes, and famous too for pickled oysters—they were made there at one time. Named for its first owner, a Dutchman called Isaac Bedloe. A fellow from New Amsterdam. . . .

"Yes," continued the traveler, "it's quite

a place—I've been there myself. There's a fort on it, and a moat around the fort, like an old castle. . . ."

But Auguste was not listening. What did he care about rabbits and forts and pickled oysters when his mind was filled with a tremendous idea—the vision of a great statue to stand on the neat little island, welcoming each ship that passed. . . .

"And in her hand must be a torch that will guide the ships that pass at night," murmured Auguste.

"For myself, I don't care much about pickled oysters," the traveler was still talking into the artist's inattentive ear.

Now during all the months that followed, while Auguste was in America, Pierre remained in France. He still continued to go, after school and on Saturdays, to the master's studio to practice modeling figures in clay. The day would come, he felt sure, when he, like Auguste, would be commissioned to carve imposing statues from blocks of stone. Had not Auguste himself started his career as apprentice to an artist? Indeed he had.

But time dragged for the boy.

Five long months had come and gone and still Auguste was in America. Pierre yearned for his master's return.

The big studio, on a dull cloudy afternoon, was none too friendly a place.

Along one end of the room was a shelf on which were many plaster casts. There were casts of feet, and hands—some of the latter clutching at empty air. There were bodiless heads whose faces were twisted as if screaming with pain. And there was a large cast of a lady whose dress had slipped down about her hips. That was not her fault, however, for she had no arms. Venus de Milo, her name was.

Nearby stood the chalky-white cast of the master's famous statue called "Genius in the Grasp of Misery."

There they all lay or stood, silent and white—gleaming unexpectedly from among gray shadows.

The clack, clack of the boy's sabots, as he crossed the floor, seemed to tag him and mock his loneliness.

But spring came at last and one day as Pierre clattered across the flags of the little courtyard to pour water on the tall plant in the green box, he heard the sound of men's voices all talking at once. Then the gate flew open with a protesting squeak.

"Pierre! Pierre!" shouted Auguste. "*Vive la France! Vive l' Amérique!* I am home!" and he greeted Pierre enthusiastically with a little peck of a kiss first on one cheek, then on the other.

With Auguste were many friends who were talking excitedly. And even after entering the studio they did not settle down as usual, to make the air blue with tobacco smoke, while they discussed the mysteries of art in general.

No, instead, everybody milled around and talked and talked without waiting to hear what anybody else might have to say.

Auguste was taking sketch after sketch from a portfolio he had brought with him, and handing them to his friends.

Pierre could get only a glimpse of the sketches and he could catch only fragments of what was being said.

"Yes, indeed," he heard Auguste say, "not only did I meet and talk to such eminent men as Cyrus Field—you know, the Atlantic Cable chap—but also President Grant himself who told me . . ."

But the rest of that story was lost to Pierre.

Presently he heard someone say, "Oh, of course! Longfellow, the poet. I know—'Under the spreading chestnut tree the village smithy stands . . .'"

"Yes, yes," interrupted Auguste. "I met *him* any number of times. In fact, I went to Boston especially to visit him."

Auguste's voice grew solemn and a bit pompous.

"His message was: 'Express for me to the people of France, all my enthusiasm for their plans. . . .'"

And so they kept on talking.

After that exciting day, when Auguste had returned from his first trip to America, things were never dull at the studio. No longer did Pierre hear the noise that his sabots made when he clattered across the studio. He was far too busy helping Auguste.

The master was soon at work modeling studies in clay from the water-color sketches he had made during his stay in America.

The clay sketches were alike in that they represented the Goddess of Liberty as a stately woman with flowing drapery, and always she held aloft a torch. But the sketches differed as to pose. In some of them the torch was in the right hand while in others it was in the left hand.

One statuette was about eighteen inches high. The Goddess held the torch in her right hand high above her head and her left hand was thrust behind her. In it she clutched a broken shackle chain.

Pierre particularly liked this one but Auguste was still dissatisfied. "It doesn't quite convey the *idea,*" he said. So he continued to try out one pose and another.

Finally he hit upon a different arrangement. The shackle chain was no longer held in the hand of the Goddess; it now lay at the base of the statue, one end of it near her forward-striding left foot. Part of the chain

was covered by her long drapery, but reappeared in front of her other foot, which had its heel raised to suggest the action of walking. In her right hand she still held the torch, but in her left hand she now carried a tablet.

This time Auguste was pleased with his work.

"At last we have it!" he exclaimed. "And who knows how long—how many scores of years—a colossal statue, in this very pose, shall stand at the gateway of the New World.

"The tablet represents the Declaration of Independence," he told Pierre; "the shackle chain—that is the broken bond of tyranny, and the torch is the symbol of the light of freedom."

This final model, which was about five feet tall, Auguste always referred to as "the sketch for the statue: 'Liberty enlightening the world.' " But Pierre already called her "big Miss Liberty" because he knew that she would not stay small—she was going to grow up.

Many visitors now flocked to the studio. One group of dignified gentlemen, in tall silk hats and formal frock coats—they were the committee—viewed the clay sketch from every angle, walking round and round while they studied it.

They talked a good deal about it and also about what they called, "our sister republic, the United States of America."

Next day Auguste said to Pierre, "The committee liked the sketch, so now we can go ahead."

Again Auguste modeled a figure in clay.

It's the same lady, thought Pierre. She's beginning to grow—she must be all of eight or nine feet tall.

Auguste spent a great deal of time and care on this new model.

"We must get into it all that the final figure should have," he told Pierre. "For this model is the one which will serve as guide for the workmen. That is, I mean it is a pattern for them to follow during the enlarging. Understand?"

"I believe so, Monsieur," said Pierre.

"In one sense, this model is my final effort . . . for if, in this small figure we make even a small mistake—perhaps the arm an inch too short—think, then, how great would be that error when the figure was enlarged many times. The arm would not be an inch too short but many feet too short. We must do our best."

It was a hard pose for the model to hold—her weight on her left foot and her arm upraised—but she patiently endured it while the artist spent hours studying the figure and shaping the drapery so that it would fall to suit him. The face of the Goddess, classic in type, he made as beautiful as he was able.

To Pierre, it was the most beautiful face he had ever seen in all his life.

Auguste often said things to Pierre which he could not quite understand, but he listened carefully just the same.

One day Auguste said, "The thought of the subject ought to be in harmony with the size of the work."

Pierre merely blinked. The master was indeed going too deep for the boy apprentice.

THE COMMITTEE

At last the clay model—*studio model* this one was called—was ready to be cast in plaster. After that Miss Liberty could go traveling about on exhibition all over France. Banquets would be held and speeches made. There would be street fairs, festivals and bazaars. But Miss Liberty would be only plaster and about nine feet tall. Money, you see, must be collected so that materials could be bought and workmen paid, and tons of materials and an army of workmen would be needed for the building of the largest statue in the world.

"For my part," said Auguste, "it is a labor of love. I want no remuneration."

The bazaar that was held near Pierre's home was officially opened with a speech by Auguste himself.

With pride gleaming in his eyes, the boy stood with the crowd and gazed up at the speaker's stand, which was draped with gay bunting. Auguste was describing his first glimpse of Bedloe's Island:

"There lay the immense city in the arms of its twin rivers, each festooned with masts and flags as far as the eye could reach. Here, I said to myself, at this gateway to the continent shall be raised the Statue of Liberty, grand as the idea which it embodies, looking out radiant over two worlds. . . ."

But speech-making was only a small part of the festivities. You could get on the merry-go-round—be whirled off at a fine speed while perched astride a fat gray rat or, if you preferred, a huge white cat—to have an exciting ride and yet land most conveniently at the very spot from which you set out. Or you could watch the puppet show and shout at Punch.

Every *sou* that was spent for fun would go to swell the "Liberty Fund." It appeared to be one's duty to invest in fun!

Throughout the towns and villages of France people were urged to contribute all that they could. School children gave *centimes* and *sous,* and so did the farmers. Some of the tradesmen gave many *francs.* Some of the wealthy folk gave large bank-notes.

And the fund grew.

Pierre, anxious to do more than donate the *sous* from his savings bank, found a way to help. He painted with yellow gilt the small white plaster casts of the Statue of Liberty and these he sold in the street markets.

"Buy Miss Liberty," he would shout and *francs* fairly rattled into his money box, so popular did the little golden figures prove to be.

By the end of the year it was formally announced that a sufficient sum had been collected and work on the great figure itself was to begin at once.

Pierre saw but little of Auguste during the weeks that followed, for the artist had many things to attend to and many helpers to direct.

First of all, a special workshop must be built—no ordinary studio would be large enough to house a giant statue which would be a hundred and fifty-two feet tall. And no one artist and his one young apprentice would be able to do all the work of making such a huge figure.

So a call was sent out for other artists, and for men who were expert in spreading plaster, and for metal-workers and for carpenters—lots of carpenters. Many men would be needed to help build the world's mightiest statue.

In earlier days Auguste had carved large statues from solid rock, but he had no intention of using anything as heavy as stone this time.

"The ship that tried to carry that much stone to America would surely sink," Auguste said to Pierre. "No, the material we use must be both light enough to transport over seas and strong enough to withstand the winds and rain. . . ."

"But statues are always made of bronze or stone," protested Pierre, "unless they're only plaster or perhaps wood. And plaster would crack, and wood couldn't withstand the rain —not for long."

Auguste laughed. "Think again, boy. You may remember that a sizable statue—San Carlo Borromeo—has already stood some two hundred years on the shore of an Italian lake. That statue was made of sheets of copper.

"Here in our workshop," continued Auguste, "we will fit together many sheets of copper—we will build the statue in sections. Then, when the Americans have prepared a massive pedestal whereon to set the towering figure, we will take apart these sections, pack them in boxes, load them on shipboard and send them across the ocean. After that, all that remains to be done is to unpack the parts, fit them together, rivet them tightly and—there you are!—a statue of durable copper."

"Like a copper skin!" shouted Pierre.

"Exactly!" cried Auguste. "A copper skin—over bones of iron for the skeleton."

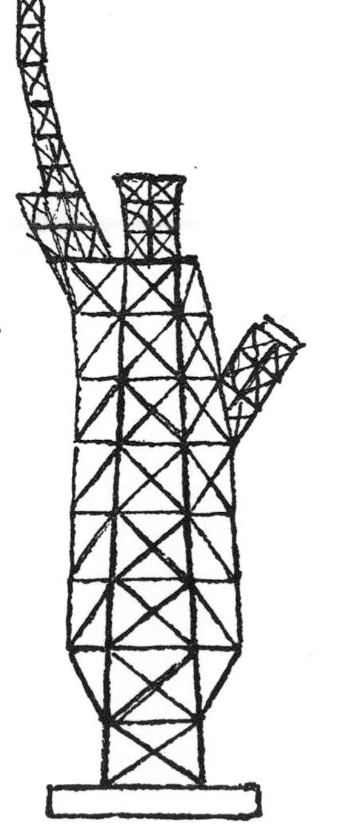

At last the actual work of enlarging the studio model was underway; and the enlarging was done, as you might say, in steps.

First there was the studio model—about nine feet tall. Then came the first copy, four times as large—it was thirty-six feet tall. From this a series of enlargements were made, not all in one piece but in sections. Each section was several times as large as the one from which it was copied. And so it went until the final set of sections, if put together, would tower one hundred and fifty-two feet high.

Now these sections, or enlarged copies, were not made of clay like the one that Auguste had modeled in his studio. Nor were they made with sheets of copper and strips of iron. No, they were made of nothing more unusual than the material that goes into the wall of your own room. They were simply built of laths nailed to a wooden frame and then covered over with a coat of plaster.

For our walls we might finish the plaster off with wall paper or a covering of paint, but for the big figure that was not necessary. She was just white, unpainted plaster.

So you see there was more than enough work for the carpenter, the man who spread plaster and the boy who carried water.

All day long the big workshop rang with the noise of hammering and sawing, and the shouts of men and boys who scrambled up and down tall ladders, or climbed high up the frame-work of what was going to be the right arm of the statue.

Auguste was nearly distracted—trying to be everywhere at once, directing, explaining and giving orders—so Pierre helped him in every way that he could.

Day after day crowds of sightseers came to the workshop to watch the men build the enormous figure. They all felt that each one

of them owned at least a tiny part of Miss Liberty. Had not their *sous* and *francs* made possible this impressive gift to the people of America?

And, since they were here, why not tell M. Bartholdi how pleased they were with the progress that had been made?

So there were always shouts of, "Monsieur Bartholdi—just a moment, please . . . can you spare the time? The Mayor of Senlis is here and wishes the honor of a word with you." Or perhaps it would be—"A member of the Guild of Plumbers is here and would appreciate it . . ." And so it went.

It was Pierre's duty to guide these visitors about the workshop. He had soon learned just how to point out what should be looked at, and to explain why the statue was being built of wood and plaster instead of bronze or stone, as statues usually were.

"This is but the huge model, *Mesdames* and *Messieurs*," he would say. "From it we will copy exactly—making the figure from many sheets of copper, riveted together and supported on the inside by an iron frame . . . a copper skin over bones of iron. . . ."

LATHS NAILED
TO A WOODEN
FRAME

Pierre never failed to say *we* very distinctly. He wanted it understood that he —Pierre, apprentice to M. Bartholdi—was an indispensable member of the workshop.

But no matter how carefully Pierre explained what was being done, there always were those, as I have said, who did not want to leave the place without hearing a few words from the famous artist himself.

Oddly enough, it was often impossible to locate the master at such times; but no matter what he was doing, Auguste never failed to drop his work to go and greet his friend, Ferdinand de Lesseps.

Auguste and Ferdinand were old friends and they both liked things made on a large scale. Years earlier they had stood side by side on the blistering sands of Egypt and gazed in awe at the Great Pyramid.

At that time Ferdinand had been in charge of the difficult task of digging a wide ditch across one hundred and four miles of desert. That mighty ditch, now filled with gleaming water, stretches like a silvery band between the Red Sea and the Mediterranean. It is the Suez Canal.

Ferdinand was more than a little impressed by the colossal statue on which Auguste was at work.

"What you are building might well be called the *eighth* wonder of the world, my friend!" he exclaimed as he looked up at the enormous hand made of laths nailed to a wooden frame.

And then there was that other man of vision—Alexandre Gustave Eiffel—whose encouraging advice was so reassuring to Auguste. A few years later, this same gifted engineer was to build the lacy tower that now rises strong and imposing, far above the streets of Paris. The Eiffel Tower, it is called, and it is more than twice as high as the Great Pyramid.

Auguste told Pierre that he counted himself a lucky man the day that M. Eiffel promised to undertake the construction of the iron skeleton for the Statue of Liberty.

Meanwhile, work on the mammoth plaster model went forward steadily.

One morning Pierre climbed up the scaffolding and out along the middle finger of the hand that was to hold the torch. He tipped his head back so far that his mouth was pulled open by the effort, and he looked straight up the length of the big first finger of the plaster hand.

It was so huge that he laughed aloud.

"What's so funny?" shouted the red-haired carpenter above the din.

"Now I know how the people of Lilliput felt when Gulliver visited them," shouted Pierre.

But at that moment several more hammers had begun to pound—the carpenter put his hand behind his ear.

"I can't hear you," he yelled.

One day the committee sent for Auguste.

"It seems," they said, "that in 1876 the Americans are to hold a special exposition in an eastern city known as Philadelphia."

"Yes," said Auguste wearily, "I am aware of the plan—it will be called the Centennial Exposition and will be in celebration of the one hundredth birthday of the republic."

"Think, then," said the committee, "how great would be the

interest of the American people if we could but send even a portion of the Statue of Liberty so that it might be shown at this exposition."

"I suppose a single section of the figure —such as the hand holding the torch— could be finished in time to send," said Auguste, but he was not enthusiastic.

"Pray let it be done," urged the committee. "It could not fail to arouse public interest. . . ."

Auguste winced. He knew what they were going to say next.

"Financial reports are not satisfactory," continued the committee. "We are pained to learn that the Americans are more than a little slow in donating funds for the building of the necessary pedestal on Bedloe's Island."

Auguste nodded sadly.

"True," he agreed.

The very next day noise and bustle in the workshop were doubled as men rushed about, preparing to shape in copper the great right hand and torch of the gigantic statue.

"It is to be shipped to Philadelphia for the exposition, and to help raise funds for the pedestal," the workers told one another.

Carpenters, and still more carpenters, were set to measuring boards and pushing saws and hammering nails. They were building huge wooden forms for the metal-workers to use.

Now those forms, built in sections, were —as to size and contour—exact copies of the big plaster hand. And when they were ready for the metal-workers, the noise in the shop began in earnest.

At first Pierre's ears ached with the din that filled the air when the metal-workers went to pounding, but after a while he got used to it.

A man would pick up a sheet of copper —perhaps a yard wide and two yards long—and place this against one of the wooden forms. Then he would begin pressing it and fitting it and pounding it, first with a heavy mallet, then with a small hammer, until the copper took on every turn and curve of the wooden form. The metal bent readily enough because it was no thicker than a five-cent piece.

When, at last, the sheet of copper had been completely shaped by the pounding, it had become a shell-like fragment of the enormous statue and exactly like the plaster model in form and size. If you could have held one of the copper parts against the plaster hand, it would have fitted over it like a glove.

Many sections were needed to make up the hand and each one was like a piece of a jig-saw puzzle—no two parts were the same.

And so it was that piece by piece, sheets of copper were pounded and shaped until there were enough metal parts for the big right hand. The copper, however, by itself was almost too flexible, so it was necessary to make each sheet rigid by backing it with iron straps. These straps were forged to fit the copper shell snugly, but between copper and iron a layer of asbestos cloth was inserted to serve as an insulator.

In the meantime, M. Eiffel and his helpers were busy, in the court ouside the workshop, constructing the network of iron that was to be the skeleton of the statue. And as each copper section was hoisted into place over the iron frame, it was made fast to the piece next to it by rivets driven through holes along the over-lapping edges.

Crowds of visitors continued to stream through the noisy workshop and Pierre still acted as their guide.

"This great hand of gleaming copper," he would shout above the din, "is soon to be shipped to Philadelphia. It is expected to arouse the interest of the Americans in our gift to them. The plan is that the great statue will be erected on Bedloe's Island, in New York Harbor, but before that is possible a pedestal must be built there by the Americans."

"How can you get that giant hand onto a boat?" asked one of the visitors.

"The hand, Mademoiselle, is made in sections," said Pierre. "The rivets will be removed, the sections marked and taken apart. They will be packed in big cases and then shipped.

"When the cases are opened in Philadelphia, the sections will be put together according to the marks and again riveted . . . it is all quite simple, Mademoiselle." Pierre's tone was a little lofty.

The young girl whom he had been addressing was about his own age and she smiled at him in a friendly way.

"I am going to America soon," she said. "I am going to live with my aunt in New

PIERRE CLIMBED OUT ALONG THE MIDDLE FINGER

York City—perhaps I shall see the hand if she takes me to the exposition in Philadelphia."

"I hope to go to New York some day," said Pierre.

Then he asked shyly, "Your name, please—what might it be?"

"Nanette," answered the girl.

In the workshop, the noise of banging and pounding did not lessen after the huge hand and torch had been packed and shipped to Philadelphia.

Auguste had told Pierre that again all work must be pushed as fast as possible so that the head of the statue—in copper—would be ready for their own Exposition Universelle to be held in 1878. So the carpenters speeded up their building of wooden forms which were patterned after the big plaster head; and the metal-workers pounded and shaped the copper parts.

Pierre thought that Auguste seemed worried and a little sad, and that was odd since the artist was now doing the very thing he had so wanted to do—making the largest statue that had ever been made in all the world. But the young apprentice understood after he had heard the carpenters talking one day while they lunched on bread and cheese, washed down with plenty of red wine.

"The Americans are not doing so well about raising that fund for the building of the pedestal, I hear," said the man in a checked shirt.

"I've heard the same," sighed the red-haired carpenter. "And t'would be a pretty pickle if the statue were all ready to present, yet the Americans could not accept the gift because they had no pedestal on which to set it."

He stopped abruptly—such a situation was too unpleasant to talk about.

The man in the checked shirt shrugged his shoulders. "I've heard it said," he remarked, "that the American newspapers throughout the country are openly hostile to the whole idea."

"But why—why should they feel like that toward a *gift* from our people?" asked Pierre.

"Perhaps it is that the Americans who live in the south and in the west—it is a vast country, you know—do not understand. I have read that many claim they do not care to give money for a pedestal so that New York Harbor may have a *lighthouse*."

"You mean that the people do not realize that the statue is a gift, not to the city of New York, but to *all* Americans, no matter where they happen to live?" asked Pierre.

"Well, that must be the difficulty," said the red-haired carpenter. "A letter from my niece came only this morning. She's been to see the copper hand at the exposition in Philadelphia; and she writes that there seems to be a general lack of understanding of our reason for building the tremendous statue."

No wonder that Monsieur Bartholdi appears worried, thought Pierre.

Week after week, work on the enormous head continued steadily. Many lustrous sheets of copper were pounded and shaped and riveted together, until the nose (it was more than four feet long) and the eyes (each one was two and a half feet wide) the mouth (a yard wide) and the face (ten feet across from ear to ear)—in fact the entire head—took form.

All this time Pierre had been growing up. He was now tall and strong, so Auguste constantly added to the responsibility given to his young assistant.

It was Pierre who supervised the work and saw that every rivet was properly fitted when the giant head of the statue was set up during the Third Universal Exposition of Paris.

As time slipped by, he had developed a strong affection for the colossal figure that he still called "big Miss Liberty." Had he not watched her grow from a mere five-foot "sketch" to this mighty statue which was slowly emerging—more or less piecemeal, to be sure—from flat sheets of copper?

Sometimes, on a warm summer evening, he would wander off to the exposition grounds to mingle with the crowds and watch people's faces as they stared admiringly up at the immense head.

"My! My! Isn't she beautiful!" someone was sure to say, and Pierre would smile at big Miss Liberty.

Perhaps it was only the shifting light, but now and again she appeared to smile slightly —oh, ever so slightly—at Pierre.

More than six years now lay between the day when Miss Liberty's head had been set up on the exposition grounds in Paris and that other memorable day when Auguste had first sailed into New York Harbor. That was the time he had suddenly seen, with his mind's eye, the stately figure of the Goddess of Liberty. During those six years he had worked hard and worked with enthusiasm, but now, at times, it must be admitted, his enthusiasm was chilled with concern.

The right hand and torch and the head of the Goddess had been completed, but there still remained the long, long task of building, in copper, the feet, the left arm and the intricate flowing drapery that fell from the shoulders to the feet of the figure.

However, it was not the amount of work still to be done that worried Auguste, but the fact that even after the statue had been finished it could not be set up on Bedloe's Island. According to reports, the American Committee for the construction of the pedestal was thoroughly disheartened over its failure to raise funds.

Apparently it would be years before the massive pedestal would be completed, so there was no longer any need to speed work on the statue. And so comparatively few men were kept on the job of building the wooden forms and beating the copper sections into shape.

One day, during the noon hour, while the men were resting, the red-haired carpenter remarked that he had news from America.

"My niece writes that the exposition in Philadelphia has come to an end, so the hand and torch have been moved to New York City. They have it set up now, she says, in a park which they call Madison Square."

"Does she say how goes the fund?" asked one of the metal-workers.

"Well, yes. She says that everyone over there is discouraged over the lack of funds with which to build the pedestal—it seems

MADISON SQUARE

their Congress in Washington has refused to help—and the whole project may have to be abandoned."

Pierre's heart was heavy. "I am told," he said, "that the hand and torch will presently be taken down and shipped back here to Paris."

"I've heard the same. Well, the work here in the shop is all but finished. The hand was shipped to the United States in '76. If it is sent back to us this year . . . let me see—1876 to 1884—that makes eight years that the Americans will have had the hand." The red-haired carpenter shrugged his shoulders.

"When the hand comes it will be bolted into place and the statue will be complete. There's nothing more that the French can do about it—it's now up to the Americans." He sighed and picked up his lunch box.

"So ends my last day on this job," he said.

Pierre turned to the man. "What is the name of your niece—the one who is in New York City?" he asked.

"Nanette," said the red-haired carpenter.

And so it was that the days became weeks, and the weeks lengthened into months. The old year died and a new year was born while big Miss Liberty, her copper skin slowly weathering to a dull, bronze color, towered patiently above the roof-tops of Paris.

Visitors from other countries and other cities continued to visit the workshop and view the Goddess of Liberty, but the people who lived in her neighborhood had become so accustomed to the sight of her that they would go about their daily affairs without even so much as a glance in her direction.

And then one day, before the new year was even a month old, the shop once more rang with the noise of hammering and men were seen climbing about the scaffolding which still surrounded Miss Liberty. They were cutting the rivets that held the copper sections together.

Word spread rapidly through the neighborhood that the statue was being taken apart.

"They are building big wooden cases in which to pack the three hundred copper sections, I've been told," said the hotel

MEN WERE SEEN CLIMBING ABOUT THE SCAFFOLDING

keeper who lived within a stone's throw of the statue.

"Does that mean that the Goddess is now to be shipped to America?" asked his next-door neighbor.

"Not so far as I know," said the hotel keeper. "I have heard nothing about any pedestal having been built. I suppose they are just packing up the statue so that it will be ready whenever the Americans care to send for it."

After the statue had been taken down and safely packed in its two hundred and more wooden cases, Auguste and his young apprentice gave all their attention to an imposing monument on which the sculptor was then at work.

One morning while Pierre was removing the wet cloths that protected the clay model, he heard Auguste coming across the courtyard.

"Pierre," cried Auguste as he flung open the studio door, "I have news from America!"

To Pierre, news from America could mean but one thing.

"The fund for building the pedestal, Monsieur!" he shouted. "Have they at last raised enough money? Are the cases to be shipped now?"

Auguste laughed. "You're right," he said, "it is news of the fund.

"You may remember that some time ago—oh, it must have been all of two years ago—I told you about the campaign which had been launched by the editor-owner of the New York *World*—a Monsieur Pulitzer? He was trying to raise money for the pedestal."

"Yes, I remember," said Pierre. "But I also remember that Monsieur Pulitzer's campaign met with discouragingly little response."

"And what was still more discouraging," said Auguste, "was the fact that while some money was contributed and work on the pedestal actually was started, the money soon gave out and that brought an end to the work.

"Well," he continued, "it seems that Monsieur Pulitzer was not one to give up an idea; and a few weeks ago—about the middle of March—just when the outlook was darkest, he began to publish a series of daily editorals in his newspaper. I have read many of them. He didn't spare his fellow-countrymen. He even warned them of the shame that all Americans must feel if they failed to accept—as he put it—'the most generous gesture one nation ever made to another.'

"And the response to those editorials was immediate! Money began pouring in from all over the country! The farmers, the tradespeople, the school children—especially the school children—sent coins——"

"Why, that's the way our people contributed to the statue-fund—farmers, tradespeople and especially the school children—they sent coins," said Pierre.

"Exactly!" cried Auguste. "And what's more, the interest of everyone has at last been captured. They are holding exhibitions and balls and sporting events . . . all for the purpose of raising funds."

Auguste thrust his arms into the sleeves of his smock and pulled it on over his head.

"If that keeps up, we'll ship the statue before long—perhaps in a month or two," said the artist as he picked up a handful of clay and pressed it into place.

"In that case, Miss Liberty will be on her way before the end of May," said Pierre.

In America, money poured into the offices of the New York *World*. No longer was there any lack of enthusiasm about contributing to the pedestal fund, for no longer did people living in other parts of the country regard the big statue as "New York's lighthouse." Joseph Pulitzer had made that clear in his many editorials.

Work on the pedestal was presently under way.

"But why wait until the pedestal has been completed? The cases need not be unpacked at once and the knowledge that the statue was stored on Bedloe's Island would stimulate interest and help to swell the fund," said the committee in America and thereupon a request was sent to the committee in France.

It was urged that the gift from the French people should be sent as soon as possible.

A short time before the ship which was to carry the statue to America was ready to sail, Auguste received a letter that gave him pleasure.

"Read this, Pierre, and note well the signature," he said as he handed the letter to his young apprentice.

The writing was fine and a little hard to decipher, and the lines ran uphill on the paper, but Pierre was able to make out the words.

"Paris, May 13, 1885," he read aloud. "My dear Mr. Bartholdi: Form to the sculptor is all, yet nothing. It is nothing without the spirit, with the idea it is everything."

And Pierre looked long at the famous signature.

"Victor Hugo!" he exclaimed, "the man who wrote *Les Misérables.*"

"Ah," breathed Auguste, "the idea—yes—'with the *idea* it is everything.' "

Odd to think that on a day, more than fourteen years earlier, a little idea—just an idea that you could neither see nor touch—had buzzed about in the back of his mind, teasing the artist . . . and now it had taken form. Without that intangible idea the gigantic statue would never have existed.

One day about the middle of June—a Friday it was—the sun beat against the mists that hung over New York Harbor. It did not succeed in drying them up, but nevertheless it did keep rain from falling on the festive scene which was taking place in the misty bay.

There was color and movement everywhere you turned your eyes. Every ship was trimmed from deck to masthead, gay flags and streamers fluttering in the wind. Along the shores more flags flapped from tall poles above roof-tops; flags trailed from ropes strung across streets; flags and bunting hung in festoons from window ledges.

Everywhere the Tricolor of France and the Stars and Stripes waved side by side.

In the sky gulls circled and screamed. Below, riding the swells of the harbor, were innumerable canoes and more than a hundred bustling tugboats. Clumsy ferryboats, cheek by jowl with graceful steam yachts and massive men-o'-war, chugged their way across crowded river traffic.

After a somewhat stormy passage of twenty-five days, the French steamship *Isère* had arrived. On board were Auguste, Pierre and the *Statue of Liberty.*

Escorted by flag ships and war vessels, and preceded by a boat carrying the President of the United States, the *Isère,* gay with fluttering flags, steamed slowly toward Bedloe's Island.

Bands were playing—you could hear both the *Marseillaise* and the *Star-Spangled Banner.* Cannon boomed and wreaths of white smoke hung over the water like clouds that had strayed too low.

Three hundred feet off the island the *Isère* dropped anchor. The gift of the people of

France had all but reached its destination.

The unloading of the cases and their transfer from ship to shore was a matter of some four weeks, so Pierre had plenty of time in which to hunt up Nanette, the niece of the red-haired carpenter. But after that he had to return to Paris because there still remained months of work before the pedestal would be ready for big Miss Liberty.

But in spite of all delays the day finally did come at last when the heroic metal figure could be erected on its pedestal of stone. So once more Pierre was needed to help with the work on Bedloe's Island.

It was a task that would call for many hours of hard work and much patient care. The intricate iron frame must be put together and the copper sections fitted and riveted, then hoisted into place and made fast by more riveting.

Icy gales would blow along that open coast at hurricane speed; and summer storms would send forks of lightning to play about Miss Liberty's mighty head. Winter cold

SOAP
BEDLOE'S
ISLAND

would make the copper skin contract and pull against the bolts that bound it to the gigantic framework, but the sun of summer would heat the metal and expand it till it buckled and bent—if care were not taken to allow just enough leeway in these bolts to let the copper plates slip a bit, one way or the other, as if Miss Liberty breathed.

Of course, the higher the statue grew—section by section—the more difficult became the work of putting it together. One time Pierre looked down from his perch on the metal framework, at the men on the ground who were moving heavy steel beams. The distance was so great that they seemed like tiny midgets.

So by dint of much hard work and endless care Miss Liberty was mounted on her pedestal. First her iron skeleton, then her copper feet, her draped legs and body, and the arm and hand holding the tablet. That tablet, by the way, bears the date, *July 4, 1776.* Then came her head and its mighty seven-point crown. And last of all the raised arm, hand and torch—the very same that, ten years before, had been sent across the Atlantic to the Centennial Exposition in Philadelphia.

During the period of construction, Pierre's legs would ache as he climbed those steep steps to inspect the work on the torch, which was nearing completion. From the torch he could look far across New Jersey. New York City spread before his eyes like a toy town. He could see the flats of Flushing, never suspecting that some day, many years hence, another great exposition would rise there, close enough for Miss Liberty to see if she turned her enormous eyes in that direction.

Great happiness filled Pierre's heart when for the last time he made his way down the many spiral steps. For tomorrow he would again see Nanette and in October Auguste was coming back to America.

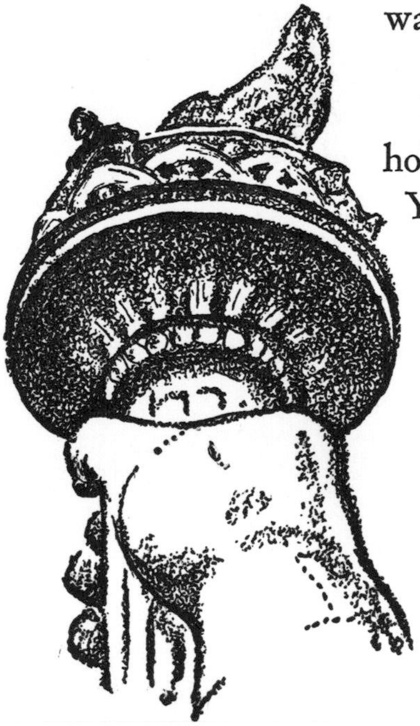

October 28, 1886, was declared a holiday, a red-letter day in New York City, for on that date the great statue, *Liberty Enlightening the World,* would be unveiled. For Auguste and all who gave thought to the matter, the occasion meant even more than the unveiling of the most colossal statue the world had ever seen. It meant an expression of friendship between two great nations.

The celebration would begin with a military parade down Fifth Avenue while a fleet of battleships paraded on the Hudson. An impressive display of fireworks at night was planned by way of climax. New York City was bent on doing honor to the event in a way worthy of the occasion.

On that morning people rose before dawn and started off to points of vantage along the line of march where regiments of soldiers would pass. Even those who need not stand on the curbstone, but had reserved seats on grandstands, even they must start betimes if they would reach their destination without danger of being caught and held up by the dense crowds that moved toward Fifth Avenue and closed in on Broadway.

The city had decked herself in miles of bunting. The Tricolor of France and the Stars and Stripes shook hands with each other every time the wind blew.

The weather, however, was not in accord with a holiday spirit, for the sky was leaden. A drizzle of fine rain fell on the city and on the closely massed sightseers. Flags and festoons of bunting hung limp and dripping, the streets were muddy, but the crowds did not seem to mind. They were out to celebrate "Bartholdi Day" and a little rain could not dampen their spirits. The fireworks would have to be postponed but all the other plans were being carried out.

Cheer after cheer greeted the marching men in uniform. And a sea of fluttering handkerchiefs, which began with the crowds at the curbing and extended to the crowds which filled every window space and all available roof-tops, was set in motion when the French veterans passed. Bands played the *Marseillaise* and followed it with *Yankee Doodle.*

The parade took hours in marching by the uncovered reviewing-stand in Madison Square which had been reserved for the notables. Auguste was there, so was Ferdinand de Lesseps—in spite of his eighty-two years and the rain. Next to Auguste was President Cleveland.

Far up the street Auguste could hear increased cheering. And as the cause of the cheering approached the reviewing-stand, the enthusiasm of the crowds increased. Presently there came into view men wearing odd-looking helmets. They were not soldiers, these men, and they were hauling after them ancient fire engines which were trimmed with flowers.

"Some of our old-time volunteer fire-laddies," Auguste was told.

Just then he caught sight of three little girls whose French uniforms were a more familiar sight to his eyes than they were to those of his American friends.

"*Les vivandières!*" he exclaimed as the three regimental canteen-bearers, accom-

panied by a fife and drum corps, stepped from line to present a silk flag to Auguste Bartholdi and flowers to the President.

Later in the day, came the momentous event of the unveiling of the statue on Bedloe's Island. The Tricolor of France, which was draped across Miss Liberty's face, was released by a twitch of the long rope which Auguste held in a hand that trembled slightly, though the veil of fog which wreathed the mighty hand and torch could not be whisked away.

Pierre and his bride, Nanette, enjoyed themselves in spite of the persistent rain. So did Auguste and the gentleman who made long and solemn speeches in honor of the occasion.

Now, all that I have been telling you about big Miss Liberty is true. A great many years have gone by since the day of the unveiling. Blizzards and violent storms have beat against her sturdy shoulders but she has not given way one inch. Several times, mid crash of thunder, lightning has struck the upraised arm, but the statue was unharmed.

Once a nearby explosion split the air and rocked the earth, but Miss Liberty remained calm. Her copper skin, her bones of iron, and her dignity were equal to the strain. Time and the salt air of the harbor have given the metal a coating of light green verdigris, but that hurts neither the copper nor her appearance.

That upraised arm did, in time, tire a little and no longer are visitors allowed to climb the long straight ladder-like steps leading up to the torch. They must be content with the view from the twenty-five windows in the crown—and that, I assure you, is well worth the climb up the one hundred and sixty-one steps of the spiral stairway.

The flame of the torch was originally made of copper and through its lower part port-holes were cut so that the light inside could be seen. All this is the way it was late in the nineteenth century when incandescent lamps were such a novelty that oil lamps were used to light the circular stairway. Some years ago the metal of the flame was replaced with leaded glass and now many powerful electric bulbs make it gleam every night, fair or stormy.

Miss Liberty has already outlived Auguste Bartholdi. He died in 1904.

The huge statue, however, seems as youthful as ever she was. The chances are she will still seem young when, one day, your children's children cross over to what is now called Bedloe Island to call on big Miss Liberty.

Now, what we see when we stand gazing up at the great statue depends entirely upon ourselves. Shall we see only two hundred thousand pounds of greenish metal that has been shaped in the form of a colossal woman?

Or shall we see back—past the metal—back to that little, yet infinitely great idea that buzzed in the head of Auguste Bartholdi?

Form is nothing without the spirit, with the idea it is everything.

SUMMARY

1834—Frederic Auguste Bartholdi, born in Colmar, Alsace.
1871—First saw New York Harbor and visualized the Statue of Liberty.
1876—Copper hand and torch sent to Centennial celebration in Philadelphia.
1877—Congress formally accepted gift from French people.
1878—Head of statue exhibited in Paris.
1883—Work on pedestal begun, then stopped.
1884—Hand and torch returned to Paris to take its place on completed statue.
1885—Work on pedestal resumed. Statue dismantled. Later shipped to Bedloe's Island.
1886—Statue erected. Unveiled October 28th.

From sea level to top of pedestal, 148 feet, 10 inches.
Height of statue to torch, 152 feet.
Length of right arm, 40 feet.
Length of index finger, 8 feet.
Points on crown, 7.
Windows in crown, 25.
Steps in spiral stairway to room in crown, 161.
Copper sections, hammered by hand, 300 sheets, 200,000 pounds.

Bedloe Island, one and two-thirds miles from the Battery, the lower tip of Manhattan Island.

Cost of statue, approximately a million francs of which every sou was contributed by the French people.

Fund raised by *The World*, $100,000 of which more than two-thirds was contributed in sums of less than a dollar each by the American people.

Total cost of pedestal, approximately, $250,000.